MODULAR COURSES IN TECHNOLOGY

MATERIALS TECHNOLOGY

Teacher's Guide

David Byrne

Kenneth Danks

Terry Hewitt

John McShea

Dr William Plumbridge

Norman Wooley

Oliver & Boyd

in association with the National Centre for School Technology

PROJECT TEAM

Director
Dr Ray Page

Co-ordinators
Roy Pickup
John Poole

Jeffrey Hall
Dr Duncan Harris
John Hucker
Michael Ives
Peter Patient

Oliver & Boyd
Robert Stevenson House
1–3 Baxter's Place
Leith Walk
Edinburgh EH1 3BB

A Division of Longman Group Ltd

ISBN 0 05 003396 4

First published 1981

Printed in Great Britain by
Spottiswoode Ballantyne Ltd.
Colchester and London.

Contents

Preface

This module is one of fourteen developed by the Schools Council Modular Courses in Technology Project, and can be used for existing courses in science, applied science, technology, technical studies, craft and design. It can also be used to build a modular course in technology, two examples of which have been tested by the Project.

The Southern Universities Joint Board and the South Western Examinations Board examine at O and CSE level respectively a scheme based on a common core of three modules (*Energy Resources, Materials Technology* and *Problem Solving*), a choice of two further modules and a major one-term project. Each module then occupies approximately ten weeks of four 35-minute periods a week.

The second scheme meets the syllabus requirements for the Cambridge University Board at O level and the East Anglian Board at CSE; it involves the use of three modules and a major two-term project, with background teaching about energy resources, the social implications of technological development, and technological problem solving. This scheme is based on modules providing for twelve weeks of four 35-minute periods a week.

This particular module is designed for a ten-week programme which, if used on the second scheme, can be extended to twelve weeks by spending more time on the mini-project work.

Further details about using the 'Modular Courses in Technology' material and the two modular technology schemes that have been developed and tested by the Project can be obtained from the Teacher's Master Manual which is published by the National Centre for School Technology in association with Oliver & Boyd.

1 Teaching the Materials Technology Module

This module aims to show the overwhelming range of materials used in everyday life as a logical array. The syllabus content has therefore been simplified to the basic metals and non-metals, between which lie the small number of semiconductor materials. Classification of materials by properties into metals and non-metals provides the basis of later work. The experimental work, though simple, will require planning and logical organisation.

Lessons on atomic structure explain simply the nature of atoms, molecules and types of bonding. This understanding is frequently used later to explain why materials exhibit different properties, and how these properties can be altered to meet different requirements, e.g. physical or environmental.

The module then considers the manufacture, processing, forming and use of various materials. The non-metals section includes many materials which exhibit similar properties of elasticity, plasticity and visco-elasticity with respect to temperature. This method of grouping brings together very diverse materials under the same umbrella.

Throughout, pupil participation in practical investigation has been encouraged so that apart from gaining knowledge about materials, the pupil will also be developing:
(a) an ordered and logical approach to experimental work;
(b) the need to question the results that are obtained;
(c) the ability to synthesise information by drawing on knowledge previously gained.
It is hoped that by stressing the technological applications of the pupil activities they will become a rewarding and enlightening experience rather than a chore. To make this impact, an environment with the correct visual and hardware resources will be needed. This in itself will not require expense but certainly organisation in order to provide the necessary practical examples of technology.

In a few cases, e.g. the extraction of metals by electrolysis, it is impractical to scale down models of industrial techniques, and it will be necessary to rely upon films or wallcharts. No apology need be made for this, since it is a technological drawback which should be understood. In other cases teacher demonstration is advised either because of the complexity of the procedure in a limited time, or the cost of materials being too prohibitive for pupil activity.

Suggestions for some of the technological applications are separately listed in the detailed notes, and this column should provide the basis for much of the teaching content. In specific cases where the technological applications directly correlate with pupil objectives this should form part of the teaching content. It is by pupils learning technological applications that this module differs from a traditional science or craft course. A conscious effort has to be made therefore to make the teaching technology orientated. In addition an awareness of economic and social implications must be included where possible, to give a rounded view of materials technology.

Throughout, pupils should be identifying ideas for their major project, and formulating these ideas through background reading and research if taking a course which culminates in a project. Suggestions for mini and major projects are included in Section 6.

The teaching material has been separated into two categories. The symbol ■ denotes subject matter applicable to all pupils (O level and CSE). The open square □ denotes subject matter required by potential O-level candidates only. Some aspects of the course can be adequately covered as homework using the relevant text in the pupil's book.

The depth of treatment can be assessed from the associated pupil's book and workbook, if any doubt exists. It should be remembered that the module is not trying to re-teach concepts already developed through previous science studies and technical courses. The intention is to build on such work and provide technological orientation.

Finally, no teachers should feel constrained to follow the teaching schedule to the letter. Rather, the schedule should be regarded as a base from which teachers can develop their own ideas to best suit the needs of their pupils.

The lesson plan, shown in summary overleaf, operates on four thirty-five minute lessons a week for ten weeks.

This is not a costly module and Section 4 gives details about 'do-it-yourself' construction for several items of equipment. Apart from the Materials Kit, most school science and craft departments will have the rest of the equipment required.

Summary of the Module

Syllabus Item		Pupil Activity	Objectives
Identification of materials in the immediate environment.	Week 1 (2 lessons)	Observation and discussion.	To be able to recognise common materials.
The comparison and grouping of solids relative to the following properties: electrical, thermal, optical, magnetic and mechanical. Materials classification into metals and non-metals.	Week 1/2 (4 lessons)	Carry out a series of simple tests to compare properties.	To be able to relate materials to their properties and applications.
Elements, compounds, atoms and molecules. Bonding forces.	Week 2 (2 lessons)	Discussion. Watch demonstrations.	To understand the nature of materials. To relate the properties of materials to the forces which hold them together.
Crystallisation and crystal shapes.	Week 3 (2 lessons)	Watch demonstration of the process of crystallisation. Construct simple crystal shapes.	To appreciate the organisation and structure of solids.
Extraction of a metal from its ore. Reduction and electrolysis.	Week 3 (2 lessons)	The reduction of lead monoxide to lead using carbon blocks.	To understand the principle of reduction and relate it to commercial practice. To understand the principle of electrolysis and its application to the extraction of aluminium.
Alloying; selection and control of properties.	Week 4 (2 lessons)	Make a tin/lead alloy and investigate the change in properties.	To make an alloy to meet specific properties of low melting point and good wettability. To recall the common applications of alloys.
Treatment and modification of structure by mechanical cold working, annealing, surface hardening, hardening and tempering.	Week 4 (2 lessons)	Experience at least one of the processes. Group discussion to follow in which pupils describe the process and change in properties.	To appreciate the effects of structure modification and relate to applications. To understand the process of work hardening in terms of grain boundaries and dislocations.
The forming of metals.	Week 5 (2 lessons)	Film and discussion on major industrial processes.	To be conversant with common manufacturing processes and appreciate the economic factors involved.
Mechanical testing.	Week 5/6 (4 lessons)	Methods of testing to be determined by equipment available in school.	To be able to interpret a force extension graph in terms of elasticity, plasticity and ductility. To understand the terms stress, strain, Young's modulus.

Syllabus Item		Pupil Activity	Objectives
Resistance to corrosion.	Week 6 (2 lessons)	Observe the rusting of steel using a ferroxyl indicator solution. Observe samples of bimetallic corrosion.	To appreciate that wet corrosion is electrical in nature and involves the movement of ions. To use the galvanic series for predicting the corrosion of adjacent metals. To be conversant with methods of preventing corrosion.
Thermoplastics, thermosets and elastomers.	Week 7 (2 lessons)	Observe samples of polymers being heated, and group together those that behave in a similar way.	To appreciate the differences in behaviour of polymers when subjected to heat. To understand the terms plasticity and cross-linking.
Changing the properties of polymers by use of fillers, extenders and foaming agents. Crystallinity and amorphism.	Week 7 (2 lessons)	Observation and discussion.	To relate change in properties to the addition of inert substances. To understand crystallinity and amorphism in terms of ordered and random alignment of the polymer chain.
The temperature/elastic behaviour of polymers.		Discuss graphs relating modulus of elasticity to temperature.	To interpret elastic modulus versus temperature graphs and relate to the forming processes.
The forming of polymers by compression, injection, extrusion, vacuum and blow moulding.	Week 8 (2 lessons)	Experience some of these processes practically or watch film. Discussion.	To understand the forming processes in terms of the application of heat and pressure. To appreciate economic factors of capital equipment, die making and materials.
Rubber. Synthetic rubbers.	Week 8 (2 lessons)	Examination of different rubbers showing the effects of vulcanisation. Discussion of the need for synthetic rubbers.	To appreciate the nature and properties of natural rubber. To understand the need for cross-linking. To relate the need for synthetic rubbers to their properties and economic factors.
Wood.	Week 9 (2 lessons)	Examine the end grain of wood under a microscope. Experience the dimensional changes that occur due to increasing moisture content by measuring samples before and after immersion in water.	To observe the cellular structure of wood and relate this to the strengths and weaknesses of the cellular shape. To observe the unequal expansion of wood and relate this to the directional swelling of the cell.
Composite materials.	Week 9 (2 lessons)	Examine examples of composites and discuss the role of the matrix and reinforcement in adapting the properties of each.	To appreciate the range of composites in everyday use.
Mini project.	Week 10 (4 lessons)	Each pupil is involved in a mini project set by the teacher.	To apply knowledge gained and explore a particular area in greater depth.

Flow Diagram

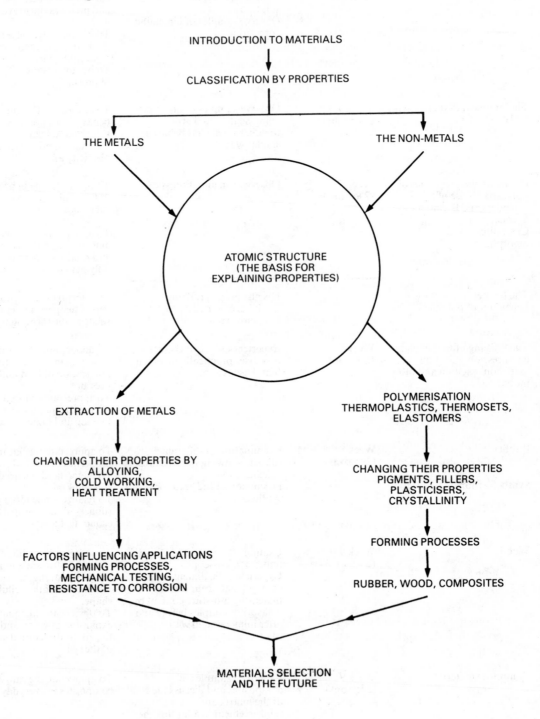

INTRODUCTION TO MATERIALS

CLASSIFICATION BY PROPERTIES

THE METALS

THE NON-METALS

ATOMIC STRUCTURE
(THE BASIS FOR
EXPLAINING PROPERTIES)

EXTRACTION OF METALS

POLYMERISATION
THERMOPLASTICS, THERMOSETS,
ELASTOMERS

CHANGING THEIR PROPERTIES BY
ALLOYING,
COLD WORKING,
HEAT TREATMENT

CHANGING THEIR PROPERTIES
PIGMENTS, FILLERS,
PLASTICISERS,
CRYSTALLINITY

FORMING PROCESSES

FACTORS INFLUENCING APPLICATIONS
FORMING PROCESSES,
MECHANICAL TESTING,
RESISTANCE TO CORROSION

RUBBER, WOOD, COMPOSITES

MATERIALS SELECTION
AND THE FUTURE

Specific Aims

After working through the course, a pupil should be able to:
(a) identify common materials;
(b) classify materials as metallic or non-metallic;
(c) understand the basic properties of materials, i.e. chemical, mechanical, electrical, thermal, optical and magnetic;
(d) explain how the properties of a material are governed by its chemical bonding and crystal structure;
(e) understand how the properties of materials can be altered by changing their chemical constitution or treating them in various ways;
(f) be conversant with particular constants, and the use of them in quantitative applications;
(g) understand the basic processes of extraction, preparation and production of materials;
(h) select materials for specific uses with regard to their properties and characteristics.

Assumed Knowledge

This course has been formulated on the premise that pupils have little or no previous experience in materials technology as it was considered that the subject was a relatively unknown topic at this stage in the average school curriculum. It was decided that it would be difficult and perhaps dangerous to make too many assumptions of knowledge, bearing in mind the diversity of courses being offered in the first three years of secondary education.

Mathematics
The mathematical knowledge required for CSE is the ability to plot, draw and interpret line graphs. Pupils must be able to add, subtract, multiply and divide decimals and calculate percentages. O-level pupils are expected to manipulate simple formulae, squares and square roots, solve simple equations and be able to manipulate very large or very small numbers using standard form, i.e. $A \times 10^{-n}$.

Science
There is a significant emphasis on scientific method, i.e. to observe, compare, record, and draw conclusions. It would be difficult to conceive of a science background that did not already give such a grounding. The depth of atomic theory will depend upon the pupils' previous learning.

Technical
From the technical sphere of knowledge, no actual ability to construct is required. Nevertheless, pupils are expected to be able to draw on their general craft experiences such as work hardening, annealing and surface hardening. Some of the syllabus items should therefore be reinforcing previous learning experiences. In addition, the ability to measure is considered vital to any technology and proficiency with a micrometer is necessary. Alternatively, this could be overcome by using dial gauges as comparators.

2 Detailed Notes for Teachers

Week No. and Content	Objectives	Technological Interpretation and Applications	Pupil Activity
1 *Introduction* (2 lessons) Identification, comparison and grouping of materials in the immediate environment	■ To be able to recognise common materials in the environment.	Constructional materials: brick, concrete, wood, glass, etc.	Make a comprehensive list of materials in the immediate environment and state the function of each material in terms of the application in which it has been found (Workbook Activity 1, Assignments 1–3).
1/ *The Properties of* 2 *Materials* (4 lessons)	■ To be able to compare and group solids relative to properties.		
Electrical conductivity	■ To be able to distinguish between those materials which are good electrical conductors and those which are good electrical insulators.	Electrical leads: wire and insulation; 13 amp plug: pins and body.	Test for electrical conductivity with a battery and bulb (Workbook Activity 2, Assignment 1.)
Thermal conductivity	■ To be able to distinguish between those materials which are good thermal conductors and those which are good thermal insulators. ■ To appreciate some of the advantages and disadvantages of thermal conduction.	Saucepan: body and handle; soldering iron: bit and handle.	1 Classify samples into insulators and conductors by placing them in boiling water. 2 Test metal samples using heat-sensitive paper. (Workbook Activity 2, Assignment 2.)
Thermal expansion	□ Numerical ability with coefficients of linear expansion.	Expansion joints, shrink fits, bimetallic strips, contraction in castings, soldering and brazing, fuse wise.	Observe the action of a bimetallic strip.
Optical properties	■ To differentiate between reflected and transmitted light. ■ To observe the importance of colour in the identification of materials.	Windows, mirrors, sunglasses, black-out curtains, matt paints.	Test for colour, reflectivity and transparency (Workbook Activity 2, Assignment 3).
Magnetic properties	■ To appreciate the forces of attraction and repulsion. □ Concept of electromagnetic induction (qualitative only).	Motors, generators, solenoids, transformers.	Observe demonstration of the electromagnetic effect of a current.

Teacher's Notes	Resources (Visual, Text, Hardware)	Lesson Requirements
Tabulate the materials under four headings: item, material, application, surface covering. It may be necessary to provide additional resources if the teaching environment is poorly served. Alternatively, set for homework.		
The Materials Kits needed for these assignments are available from the Surplus Buying Agency (see Appendix C for address). Each kit contains ten 3 mm rods of the materials to be tested, and should be used one between two pupils. The first four assignments can be done in any order to help avoid the necessity for large quantities of equipment. The electrical conductivity test-rig can be built relatively cheaply. See Section 4 for details.		Materials Kits and electrical conductivity test-rig. Materials Kits, tripods, gauze, beakers of water. Bunsens (fishtail for No. 2 if available) and heat-sensitive paper.
Demonstrate the mechanical movement of a bimetallic strip using a room thermostat, automatic kettle, flasher unit of a car or car thermostat. Some automatic street lamps are operated by a light-dependent resistor heating an element in contact with a bimetallic switch. Vocabulary may be a problem for less able pupils when trying to describe variations in tone or colour.		Bimetallic strip and appropriate method of heating. Materials Kits and fine wire wool.
Demonstrate the forces of magnetism – unlike poles attract and like poles repel. Pass an electric current through a wire and hold over a small plotting compass. Note the swing of the compass needle caused by the electromagnetic effect of a current.		Two magnets, length of copper wire, battery and plotting compass.

Week No. and Content	Objectives	Technological Interpretation and Applications	Pupil Activity
1/ *The Properties of* 2 *Materials (cont.)* Mechanical properties	■ To understand that materials deform if subjected to sufficient force.		Observe demonstration and take part in discussion.
(a) Elastic and plastic deformation	■ To be able to differentiate between the elastic and plastic properties of a material.		
(b) Ductility	■ To relate the extensive deformation properties of metal to the term ductility.	Deep pressings, e.g. kitchen sinks, car bodywork, kitchen pots and pans.	
(c) Strength	■ To understand the term strength.		
(d) Toughness	■ To be able to recall the meaning of the term toughness. ■ To appreciate the relative toughness of materials.	Window glass is brittle, window frames are tough. Laminated windscreens.	Reverse bend test to fracture the rods (Workbook Activity 2, Assignment 4).
(e) Hardness	■ To appreciate hardness variations in materials.	Cutting tools: pencil sharpener, high carbon steels, carbide tipped tools, diamond tipped tools. Abrasives: glass, garnet, corundum.	Scratch test for relative hardness (Workbook Activity 2, Assignment 5).
Materials classification into metals and non-metals	■ To synthesise information and to be able to draw conclusions from test results.		Discuss experiments and look for similar groupings through the different tests.
2 *Atomic Structure* (2 lessons) Elements and compounds Atoms and molecules	■ To recall that molecules are formed by systematically assembling two or more atoms.	The structure of material.	Listen to a basic outline of atomic theory.
Inside different atoms	■ To understand what forces hold material together.		Electrostatic experiment to show attractive forces. Rub comb in hair and pick up pieces of paper.
Ionic bonding	■ To recall the concept of ions in solution.		
	■ To appreciate that copper chloride is a compound and that the bonding is essentially electrical in nature.	Electroplating and refining of metals. Corrosion of metals.	Watch demonstration of electroplating a carbon covered non-metallic article, e.g. a flower, using a copper chloride bath.

Teacher's Notes	Resources (Visual, Text, Hardware)	Lesson Requirements
Discuss the ways in which a material may be deformed. Use a piece of spring steel to illustrate the elastic properties. Exert sufficient force to produce permanent deformation in the spring steel and thereby illustrate the plastic property. Emphasise that all materials exhibit some degree of elasticity and plasticity.		A piece of spring steel.
Strength is the ability to withstand a particular type of repeated deformation force.		
Do not carry out the toughness test before electrical and thermal conductivity have been assessed. Toughness to be considered as the energy required to fracture. Safety aspects, with the glass rod particularly, must be considered. You may wish to demonstrate the toughness of glass.		Materials Kits, vice, lever, angle gauges and face shields.
Place one edge of a rod on to the side of another. Does the rod slide or bite? Harder materials bite.		Materials Kits.
Results will divide clearly into metallic and non-metallic groups with carbon as the prominent exception since its shows semiconductor properties. Mention silicon and germanium as two other common semiconductors which have not been included for economic reasons.		
Introduce concepts of elements and atoms. This knowledge should already have been covered in science, and the depth should be varied to suit the group. Atoms consist of a dense, tiny but very heavy nucleus which is positively charged. Orbiting the nucleus are very light negatively charged electrons. In metals, some electrons are loose and can be moved or even lost by the atoms.	'Time Life' periodic table. Film *Evidence for Atoms and Molecules* (EFVA). Wallchart *Earth's Resources* from Pictorial Charts Educational Trust.	
The experiment is a simple introduction to the forces which hold material together.		Comb and paper.
On the basis of experimental results it can be explained that copper chloride crystals are made up of positively charged copper particles, joined to negatively charged chlorine particles. It is the attraction between the copper and chlorine particle which holds the crystal together. If an intelligent pupil asks why the bonds fail in water it is because of the weakening effect of water on the bond strength.	Wallcharts *Structure – Atomic and Ionic* and *Chemical Bonding* from Pictorial Charts Educational Trust.	DC source for electroplating, copper chloride solution, beaker, a non-conductive article, colloidal graphite.

Week No. and Content	Objectives	Technological Interpretation and Applications	Pupil Activity
2 *Atomic Structure (cont.)*	■ To relate the nature of ionic bonds to the attractive force of unlike electric charges.		
Covalent bonding	□ To classify the nature of covalent bonding as the sharing of electrons.	Bonding of organic molecules such as cellulose. Bonding of ceramics.	Discussion.
Metallic bonding	□ To classify the metallic bond as having free electrons.	Protective coatings. Electrical and thermal conductivity.	Put a drop of water on to a series of materials, some electrovalent, some covalent.
3 *Crystallisation* (2 lessons) Molecular structure and crystal lattices	■ To appreciate the organisation and structure of solids. ■ To link the idea of structure to the existence of small particles.	Diamond cutting tools. The casting of metals.	Observe the growth of silver crystals. Examine a variety of solids to look for crystal structure.
Crystal shapes	□ To relate the shapes face-centred and body-centred cubic and close-packed hexagonal to the ductility of common metals.	The formability of metals.	Assemble cubic and hexagonal structures from card (Workbook Activity 3) or construct crystal shapes using plasticine or polystyrene balls and cocktail sticks.

Teacher's Notes	Resources (Visual, Text, Hardware)	Lesson Requirements
Discuss the nature of the covalent bond as the process by which electron shells can be filled.		
Ionic materials dissolve. Metallic materials corrode. Put a drop of water on polished mild steel and wipe off in ten seconds. The start of the corrosion will be visible. Ionic materials will need to be coloured to indicate that they are dissolving. Exclusion of an electrolyte is the important characteristic of protective coatings. Only elevated temperatures are capable of dissociating electrovalent materials. Emphasise the importance of free electrons in the metallic bond that lead to electrical and thermal conductivity.		Scrap of polished mild steel, a coloured salt, e.g. copper sulphate.
Dissolve a grain of silver nitrate in a drop of fresh water. Place a freshly cleaned piece of copper wire into the solution and observe the dendrites growing around the copper wire. This is an excellent demonstration if a 'Halight 300' slide projector is available. It is worthwhile trying the experiment beforehand to judge the rate of dendritic growth (starts within two minutes).	Film *Considering Crystals* (Unilever). Wallchart *Shapes of Crystals* from Pictorial Charts Educational Trust.	Silver nitrate crystal, short length of copper wire, wire wool, projector.
Crystal structure is clear in galvanised sheet, or brass door handles which have been well used over the years.		Galvanised steel, old brass door handles, etc.
Duplicate the cube and hexagonal outlines from Section 4 in the Guide onto thin card. Arrange pupils in groups, the idea being that each pupil will make one of the shapes and then combine with others in the group to make either a pack of hexagonal prisms or cubes. Groups can later exchange packs in order to complete the questions in the Workbook activity.		Craft knives, steel rules, sellotape, rubber bands, sheets of thin card with cube and hexagonal outlines.
Illustrate that many small cubic shapes when stacked together give a larger shape of the same type. It should be made clear that many crystals are, however, irregular on a large scale despite the regularity of the unit shapes.		
As an alternative to the Workbook activity, pupils may construct shapes using plasticine or polystyrene balls and cocktail sticks. Be sure to relate this to reality, i.e. cocktail sticks do not hold particles together. Point out: a) the limited number of unit shapes possible; b) the order of size of the particles.		Alternatives: (a) plasticine and cocktail sticks; (b) polystyrene balls and cocktail sticks; (c) ping-pong balls and 'Blu-Tack'.

Week No. and Content	Objectives	Technological Interpretation and Applications	Pupil Activity
3 *The Extraction of Metals* (2 lessons) Reduction The production of iron Electrolysis The production of aluminium	■ To observe the principle of reduction and relate this to commercial practice. □ To be able to interpret the reactivity series as a basis for the reduction process. □ To understand the principle of electrolysis and its application to the extraction of aluminium.	Covalent bonding in commercial extraction. Ionic bonding in commercial extraction.	Reduction of lead oxide by carbon. (Workbook Activity 4, Assignment 1). Discuss the economic factors of the extraction processes.
4 *Alloying* (2 lessons) The melting point of alloys The melting of tin/lead alloys	■ To be conversant with the applications of common alloys and their properties. ■ To make an alloy to meet specific properties of low melting point and good wettability. □ To be able to interpret simple equilibrium diagrams involving eutectics.	Passivity – domestic stainless steel; strength – aluminium based alloys; eutectics – solders and welding rods, fire sprinklers, nichrome resistance wire, coinage.	Comparison of the melting point and wettability of lead, tin and a 1:2 lead/tin alloy (solder) followed by discussion of results and implications for other alloys (Workbook Activity 4, Assignment 2).
4 *Cold Working and Heat Treatment* (2 lessons) Mechanical cold working Dislocations Annealing Heat treatment (a) Surface hardening	■ To appreciate the effects of work hardening. □ To understand the process of work hardening in terms of grain boundaries and dislocations. ■ To appreciate that annealing has the opposite effect to cold working. ■ To illustrate the addition of a non-metal to alter the structure and hence the properties. □ To verify the importance of carbon content in steels.	Crystal lattice modification by dislocation. Pressings, e.g. car bodies. Shot-peening, e.g. connecting rods, crankshafts. Surface structure, modification by diffusion, carburising and nitriding.	Place a strip of annealed copper in a vice. Bend it through a right angle and try to straighten it (Workbook Activity 5, Assignment 1). Re-anneal the copper by heating to a dull red (Workbook Activity 5, Assignment 2). Surface harden a piece of mild steel. File surface until through the 'case' (Workbook Activity 5, Assignment 3).

Teacher's Notes	Resources (Visual, Text, Hardware)	Lesson Requirements
Simplify the chemical details as much as possible, e.g. lead oxide + carbon → lead + carbon dioxide. Precautions must be taken to prevent molten lead being scattered by over-enthusiastic use of the blowpipe. Face shields are necessary. Mineral source to be mentioned. Note the fire danger when storing hot carbon blocks. Introduce the 'order of chemical reactivity': magnesium, aluminium, carbon, zinc, iron, tin, lead, copper. Metals lower than carbon can be extracted by reduction with carbon. Mention that metals can be refined further – the degree of refining being important.		Carbon blocks, Bunsens, blowpipes, lead monoxide powder, face shields.
Melt the lead and then add the tin 2:1 by weight. Note safety with molten metal, use a plate with sides or a rim. Do not use a 'tin lid' as it will upset the wettability. Slight hazard with lead should be noted.		Bunsens, tripods, tongs, crucibles, balance, mild steel sheet, granulated tin and lead, face shields.
Demonstrate the process of work hardening. Use a ball-bearing model to illustrate dislocations moving through the crystal lattices. A ball-bearing model consists of many small bearings held in a frame and can be used on an overhead projector.		Ball-bearing model. Strips of copper, vices.
The annealing process can be shortened by quenching the hot copper in water. Pupils should realise though that this would harden some steels.		Work-hardened copper, tongs, face shields, Bunsens, beakers of water.
Heat the mild steel to red heat and then dip in the 'Kasenit'. Heat to red heat and quench. The case is hardened. Compare this with industrial process of carburising where the case is deep enough for the process to be followed by tempering to reduce brittleness. Discuss the importance of carbon content in the heat treatment of steels.		Mild steel rods from the Materials Kits, carburising powder 'Kasenit', tongs, Bunsens, face shields, vices, files.

Week No. and Content	Objectives	Technological Interpretation and Applications	Pupil Activity
4 *Heat Treatment (cont.)* (b) Hardening and tempering The heat treatment of aluminium alloys	☐ To understand basic heat-treatment processes and their effect on properties. ☐ To know that aluminium alloys can also be heat treated (process not necessary).	Modification of crystal lattice in heat-treatable steels. Cutting tools.	Harden and temper a piece of silver steel (Workbook Activity 5, Assignment 4).
5 *Forming Methods* (2 lessons) Casting Hot working Cold working	■ To be conversant with basic forming processes. ■ To interpret these processes with a simple understanding of economic factors.	Rolling, casting, drop forging, sintering, extrusion, drawing. Properties of fluidity in casting, and plasticity in mechanical working.	Film and discussion on the relative economics of the forming processes.
5/ *Mechanical Properties* 6 (4 lessons) The tensile test Calculations of stress, strain and Young's modulus The hardness test	■ To be able to interpret a force/extension graph in terms of elasticity, plasticity, ductility. ☐ To understand Young's modulus $= \dfrac{\text{stress}}{\text{strain}}$. ☐ To be able to interpret a stress/strain curve. ☐ To appreciate the difference between stress/force, strain and extension.	Applications of mechanical properties. Non-destructive testing for product control.	Basic mechanical testing of tensile strength. Basic mechanical testing of hardness.

Teacher's Notes	Resources (Visual, Text, Hardware)	Lesson Requirements
Place the silver steel rod in a vice and tap with a hammer to show how tough and springy it is. Harden it by heating to cherry red, quench in beaker. Test again to show how hard and brittle it has become. To temper, first polish the hardened sample with the emery cloth, then reheat until purple oxide appears. Quench and test again to show increased toughness. It should be emphasised that other metals can be heat treated to modify properties. Aluminium alloys are important. The four assignments in Activity 5 can be divided between the class and followed by a report-back by pupils.	Wallchart *The Hardening and Tempering of Carbon Steels* and film *The Hardening and Tempering of Steel* (BP).	Silver steel rods from the Materials Kits, emery cloth, Bunsens, tongs, files, vices, hammers, face shields.
Casting is the cheapest method of production. Mechanical working increases production costs through time and labour.	Film *The Forming of Metals* (Shell). Wallchart *Zinc Alloy Die Casting* from the Zinc Alloy Die Casters Association.	
Methods of testing to be determined by equipment available in individual schools, and for this reason no specific assignments have been included in the workbook. However, details of suitable apparatus appear in Section 4 under the heading 'Simple Hardness Test Equipment'.		Equipment dependant upon facilities.

Week No. and Content	Objectives	Technological Interpretation and Applications	Pupil Activity
6 *Corrosion* (2 lessons) Electrochemical behaviour in aqueous corrosion Bimetallic corrosion Methods of preventing corrosion	■ To appreciate that wet corrosion is electrical in nature. □ To be aware of the galvanic series for predicting corrosion of adjacent metals. □ To know about anodic and cathodic regions and the movement of ions. ■ To be conversant with methods of preventing corrosion.	Deterioration of metals in service. Action of dry cell battery. Sacrificial anodes. Galvanizing, plating, anodising, painting, cellulosing, enamelling, inhibitors.	Use ferroxyl indicator solution to illustrate the electrical nature of corrosion (Workbook Activity 6, Assignment 1). Observe samples of sacrificial anodes (Workbook Activity 6, Assignment 2).
7 *Polymers* (2 lessons) Thermoplastics, thermosets and elastomers	■ To appreciate the difference in behaviour of thermoplastic, thermoset and elastomer materials when subjected to heat. ■ To understand the terms polymerisation and cross-linking.	Thermoplastics – the recycling of polymers. Thermosets – electrical and thermal insulators. Polymerisation of cyanoacrylate glues with water vapour.	Observe samples of polymers while they are being slowly heated. Divide the materials into groups that exhibit similar characteristics (Workbook Activity 7, Assignment 1).
7 *Changing the Properties of Polymers* (2 lessons) The use of fillers, extenders, pigments or foaming agents The stabilisation of polymers against ultraviolet light Crystallinity and amorphism	■ To relate the change in properties to the addition of inert substances. □ To understand crystallinity and amorphism in terms of ordered and random alignment of the polymer chains. □ To apply the properties of each structure to its applications.	Fillers and extenders improve mechanical, electrical or thermal properties. Carbon black is used in polyethylene refuse sacks to stabilise against ultraviolet degradation. Packaging materials. Upholstery foams. Materials development to give final properties for a design application. Quartz and optical glass. Crystalline hinges for a case which requires amorphous sides. Fibre technology. Packing-case strapping.	Observation and discussion. Either knead and roll putty and then try to break it, noting the alignment that takes place, or observe a sample of polystyrene that has been stretched and note the change of optical characteristics and directional preference to tearing.

Teacher's Notes	Resources (Visual, Text, Hardware)	Lesson Requirements
Prevention tests would be a long term investigation project. The teacher should apply the ferroxyl indicator solution to the pupil's steel. Have samples of sacrificial anodes in brine available for observation, e.g. nail wrapped in zinc and another wrapped in copper. See Section 5 for supplementary notes on crevice corrosion – this is another long term experiment. Discuss methods of preventing corrosion.	Pamphlet 'The Rusting of Steel', Unilever Laboratory Experiment No. 9. Book *Corrosion – Attack and Defence*. *Project* magazine No. 5, Autumn 1976, 'Is Rust a Must?'.	Ferroxyl indicator solution (see Section 5), steel sheet, emery cloth. Sacrificial anodes previously immersed in brine.
Extremely important to provide adequate ventilation. Introduce pupils to the need for safety when handling polymers. Explain the polymerisation of molecules. Explain the effects of cross-linking by reference to covalent bonding. Samples should be heated to their glass transition stage where appropriate (max. 200°C). Try to drop the term 'plastics' and use the word 'polymers'.	ICI wallchart *How Plastics Help Us* and booklet *What are Plastics?* BP wallcharts *How We Use Plastics* and '*Which Plastics?*'.	Hot plates or Bunsens, steel sheets, tripods, face shields, sample remains from test rods supplemented by scraps of some thermosets, e.g. formica, phenolic, polyester, bakelite, etc.
The common names of polymers have been adhered to in the pupil text but some of the corresponding chemical names are given in the table on pages 63–4. Demonstrate the polymerisation of polyurethane foam if appropriate ventilation is available. Avoid breathing the vapour and avoid contact with skin and eyes. Discuss the use of flexible and rigid foams, and the associated fire hazards. Glass to be treated as an amorphous polymer. Note that crystal glass is not crystalline. Crystallinity confers flexibility with strength.		Two part polyurethane foam, extractor unit or fume cupboard, face shields. Sample of putty, prestretched polystyrene or polypropylene.

Week No. and Content	Objectives	Technological Interpretation and Applications	Pupil Activity
7 *Changing the Properties of Polymers (cont.)* The temperature/elastic behaviour of polymers Amorphous, crystalline and cross-linked polymers	☐ To appreciate the difference between crystallinity in metals and polymers (less ordered arrangement). ■ To appreciate rigidity versus temperature properties. ☐ To interpret graphs relating the rigidity of amorphous, crystalline and cross-linked materials with temperature, and apply this knowledge in the forming processes.	Unsuitability of rubbers at low temperatures due to brittleness. Softening of polymers during forming. The rigidity of these materials with temperature.	Discuss graphs relating modulus of elasticity to temperature. Observe how different polymers may have varying temperature gradients but follow similar elastic behaviour.
8 *The Forming Processes* (2 lessons) Compression moulding, injection moulding, extrusion, vacuum forming, blow moulding The economics of the forming processes	■ To recall each of the five processes. ■ To understand the forming processes in terms of the application of heat and pressure. ☐ To appreciate the economic factors of capital equipment, die-making and materials.	Plasticity and visco-elasticity as essential properties of polymer materials in industrial forming processes.	Observe the manufacture of polymers either practically or on film. Make a critical assessment of at least two forming processes (Workbook Activity 7, Assignment 2).
8 *Rubber* (2 lessons) Vulcanisation Synthetic rubbers	■ To appreciate the nature and properties of natural rubber. ■ To understand the need for cross-linking and how this link is responsible for the material's characteristics. ■ To relate the need for synthetic rubbers to their properties and economic factors.	Tyre manufacture. Use of fillers such as carbon black to improve the mechanical properties of synthetic rubbers and the hardness of natural rubber. Aircraft tyres use graphite fillers to produce a rubber of low electrical resistance which permits rapid discharge of static electricity.	Examination of different rubbers including latex, showing the effects of vulcanisation.

Teacher's Notes	Resources (Visual, Text, Hardware)	Lesson Requirements
Explain the four areas of behaviour on the graph (Fig. 6.7 in the pupil text).

Tie up the application in terms of rigidity.

A simple demonstration of the change in elastic properties with temperature is to put a strip of cellulose acetate (OHP material) in boiling water whereupon it will lose its stiffness. Note that when polymers are formed they do not melt since they would decompose chemically. | Figure 6.7 in the pupil text. | |
| Summarise each method of forming in terms of the application of heat and pressure. | ICI Schools Publication No. 9, *What are Plastics?*.

BP wallchart *Shaping Plastics*.

ICI films *Working with Thermoplastics* and *Polymers*. | Facilities for forming polymers or film showing the processes.

Examples of commercial products. |
| Explanation of the cross-linking in terms of sulphur atoms acting as flexible links between the rubber molecules.

Silicone rubbers – mention that molecules of silicones are based upon rows of atoms linked by oxygen atoms. Point out the chemical similarity of carbon and silicon.

Discuss and if possible demonstrate the brittleness of rubber at low temperature by immersion in liquid nitrogen.

A sample of latex is easily obtained from 'Copydex' and can be coagulated by pouring it into methanol or acetone.

Without reinforcement, the strength of synthetic rubbers is so low that they would be technologically unacceptable materials. This contrasts with natural rubber which has a higher tensile strength without carbon black; the filler is however necessary to improve other properties, e.g. hardness. | Films *Rubber in Engineering* (Golden Films) and *Rubber by Design* (Shell).

Book *The Science of Rubber* (Dunlop Education Service). | Samples of rubber: ebonite, hard rubbers, raw and natural rubber. |

Week No. and Content	Objectives	Technological Interpretation and Application	Pupil Activity

9   *Wood* (2 lessons)
      Structure
 	
      Calculating moisture
      content
	■ To observe the cellular structure of wood.
	
	 ■ To relate the strengths and weaknesses in terms of cellular shape.
	
	 □ To observe the unequal expansion of wood and relate this to directional swelling of the cell.
	 □ Numerical ability relating the movement of wood to moisture content.
		Seasoning of timber.
		
		 The expansion and contraction of wood.
		
		 Constructional applications – manufactured boards, methods of furniture assembly.
			Observe the end grain of samples of wood (Workbook Activity 8, Assignment 1).
			
			 Observe the compression test of straws that have been glued together.
			
			 Calculate the percentage increase in moisture content of a sample after it has been pressure-cooked (Workbook Activity 8, Assignment 2).

9   *Composite materials*
      (2 lessons)
      Layer composites
      Particle composites
	■ To appreciate the range of composites in everyday use.	Layer composites (polymer): Formica, GRP, Tufnol, rayon reinforcement of tyres, oxy-acetylene hosepipes. Layer composites (metal): copper-clad saucepans, bimetallic strips. Particle composites: concrete, reinforced concrete, carbon black in car tyres, papier-mâché.	Observation and discussion of the role of matrix and reinforcement in adapting the properties of each.

10 *Mini project* (4 lessons)	■ To apply knowledge gained in the module and explore a particular area in greater depth.		Read the final chapter in the pupil text in preparation for the mini project.

Teacher's Notes	Resources (Visual, Text, Hardware)	Lesson Requirements
Explain the affinity of cellulose for water as a result of hydroxyl bonds in the cellulose molecule. Relate this to the seasoning and constructional techniques that are applied to wood. Explain that lignin is the other ingredient predominant in wood. Use bamboo as a good example of the fibrous nature of cellulose. Explain the thermoplasticity of wood in terms of its lignin content.	Wallcharts *Derivatives of Wood, Moisture Content* and *Utilisation* from the Timber Research and Development Association.	Samples of balsa wood or pine, stereo microscope or hand lens.
Demonstrate the compression testing of drinking straws and explain the analogy between straws and the structure of wood.

Consider wood as a composite material.

The teacher should take charge of the pressure-cooking of the wood samples. If a pressure cooker is not available, dry out wood specimens thoroughly beforehand and allow to soak in a container to absorb water. | | Drinking straws, PVA glue, compression tester (see Section 4), kilogram masses up to 30 kg.

Wood samples as above, micrometers or dial gauges, pressure cooker or oven, balance. |
| Have some samples of composites available for observations. | | Samples of Formica, GRP, Tufnol, concrete, bimetallic strips. |
| See Section 6 for suggestions for mini projects. Prepared resource material for pupils will allow familiarisation with the task beforehand. Success with mini projects will rarely be achieved without a high degree of organisation. | Project briefs. | Dependant upon project brief. |

3 List of Equipment

1   Equipment already available in science or craft departments
Balance
Beakers, crucibles and tongs
Blow pipes
Bunsen burners, tripods, pipe clay triangles and gauzes
Carbon blocks
Crystallising dishes or microscope slides
DC supply or power packs
Emery cloth
Face shields or goggles
Files and hammers
Fume cupboard or extractor unit
Hand lenses or binocular microscopes to $\times 10$ max.
Kasenit powder
Kilogram masses to approx. 30 kg
Mechanical testing equipment for hardness and tensile strength
   (see Section 4 for equipment that can be made in school)
Plastics moulding machines if available
Thermometers ($0-100°C$)

2   Other equipment
Compression jig for testing straws (see Section 4)
Electrical conductivity test rig (see Section 4)
Levers
Oven or pressure cooker

3   Materials to be obtained
The Materials Kit which contains 3 mm diameter rods of various materials can be obtained from the Surplus Buying Agency (see Appendix C for address). One kit should be used between two pupils.

4 Notes on Constructing Equipment

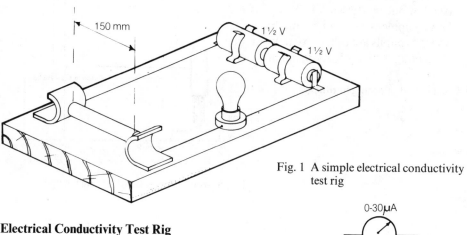

Fig. 1 A simple electrical conductivity test rig

Electrical Conductivity Test Rig

A simple or complex test rig can be built relatively cheaply for use in Activity 2, Assignment 1. Figures 1 and 2 give details of both.

Fig. 2 A more complex test rig

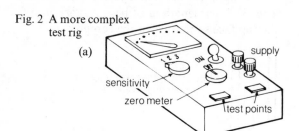

(a)

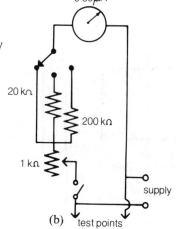

(b)

'Reverse Bend' Test Equipment

This is needed in Activity 2, Assignment 4. The procedure for using the rig is shown in Fig. 3. Chamfering the end of the tube avoids the need for angle guages. Figure 4 shows the lever used to bend the sample.

Fig. 3 'Reverse bend' test equipment

Fig. 4 The lever used to bend the sample

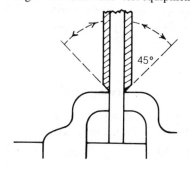

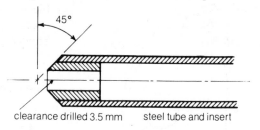

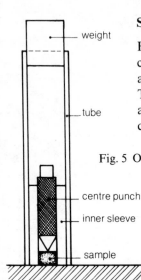

Simple Hardness Test Equipment

Figures 5 and 6 show two methods of carrying out this test which pupils are asked about in Activity 4, Assignment 2. This equipment will also be suitable for the activities pupils are asked to carry out after completing Activity 5, Assignment 4.

Fig. 5 One method of testing hardness

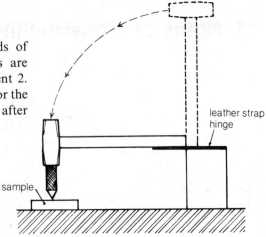

Fig. 6 Another method of testing hardness

Compression Jig for Testing Straws

Figure 7 shows a possible compression jig for testing straws in the first part of Week 9. The guide bar length must be just short of the top face so that when the compression

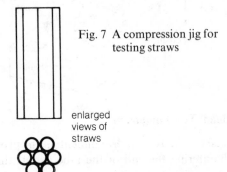

Fig. 7 A compression jig for testing straws

enlarged views of straws

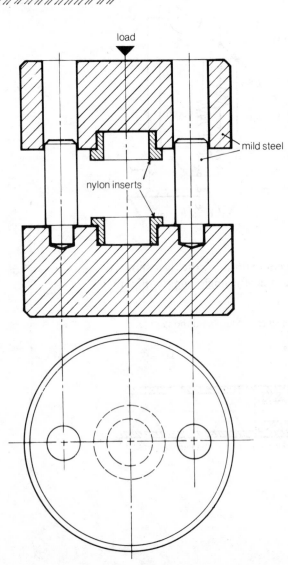

tester is fully closed it avoids contact with the weights. Approximately 30 kg will be necessary to compress straw samples bonded with PVA glue.

Development Drawings for Crystal Models

These should be duplicated onto thin card and handed out to pupils for use in Activity 3 (see Fig. 8 opposite).

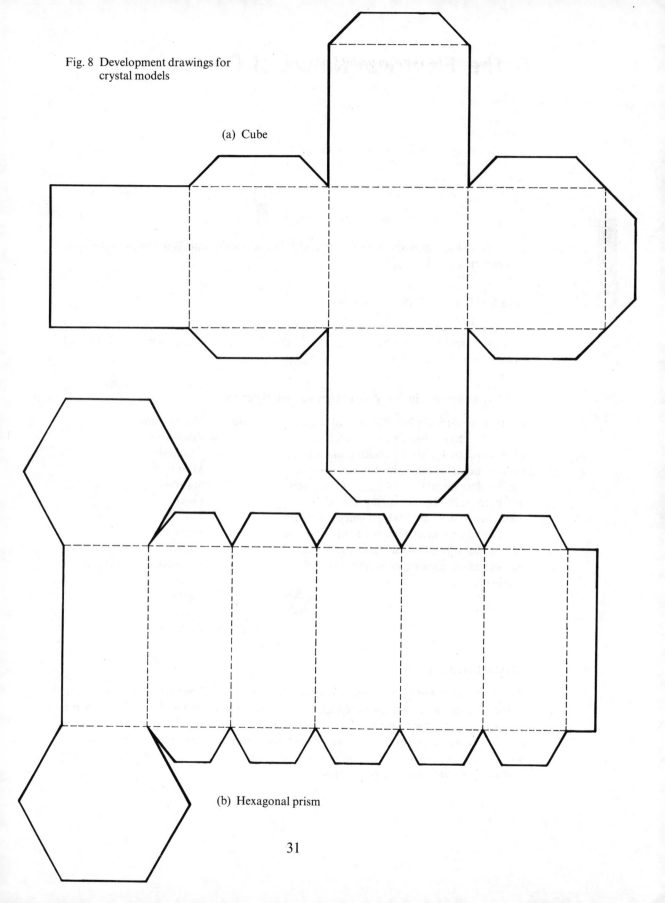

Fig. 8 Development drawings for crystal models

(a) Cube

(b) Hexagonal prism

31

5 The Electrical Nature of Corrosion

These notes are supplementary to Section 2, Week 6 and Pupil Workbook Activity 6, Assignments 1 and 2.

Details of Ferroxyl Indicator Solution

Dissolve 5 g of sodium chloride and 0.5 g of potassium ferricyanide in 100 cm³ of distilled water and add 0.5 cm³ of phenolphthalein solution. Add more distilled water to make a total of 250 cm³.

The Galvanic Series in Sea Water/Aqueous Salt Solution

A galvanic series is a list of metals arranged in order such that there will be the least electrical activity, in a given aqueous environment, between any adjacent pair in the list. Any metal will form a corrosion cell and become the anode when paired with any metal below it. Conversely, it will become the cathode when paired with any metal above it. The further apart two metals in the list may be, the greater the electrical activity causing corrosion.

Base: Magnesium
Zinc
Aluminium
Mild steel
Stainless steel, active
Lead
Tin
Brass
Nickel
Stainless steel, passive
Silver
Carbon
Gold
Noble: Platinum

Crevice Corrosion

This is interesting but not essential knowledge for either CSE or O level. Two positions in the galvanic series are allocated to stainless steel. Corrosion will occur if oxygen is not readily available to establish and maintain the oxygen film. Stainless steel is then active and occupies a position comparable with ordinary steel in the galvanic series. The following long term experiment demonstrates the process of crevice corrosion caused by a restricted supply of oxygen.

Details of Experiment

The taut rubber band makes an angle of about 20° which is bisected by the strip of stainless steel. The steel can be conveniently held by squeezing the metal into the wood using a vice.

Set this aside for occasional inspection over a six- to eight-week period. During this time it may be necessary to replace water that has evaporated. It is also desirable to renew the solution about twice a week after corrosion has begun.

The surface of the stainless steel will remain passive and will be held at a relatively high (cathodic) potential. A corrosion cell will be active where close contact of the rubber band prevents access of oxygen to the edge of the steel. Here the steel will assume a relatively low (anodic) potential. The cathode is large, the anode small. Corrosion current density, therefore, will be high and the result will be the progressive formation of a slot the width of the rubber band. This demonstrates that stainless steel must remain in its passive state if its properties are to be fully exploited.

Fig. 9 Experiment to demonstrate crevice corrosion

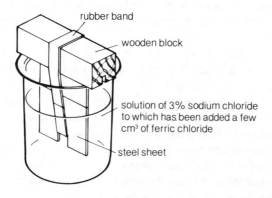

rubber band

wooden block

solution of 3% sodium chloride to which has been added a few cm³ of ferric chloride

steel sheet

6 Project Work

Suggestions for Mini Projects

1 *Steam Bending of Wood*

Furniture is often made of strips of wood that are steam bent and laminated together. Investigate the following aspects of steam bending, using samples of wood 200 mm × 2 mm:

(a) the minimum radius to which it can be bent before noticeable fracture begins;

(b) the optimum time that the wood needs to be in the steam prior to its being shaped;

(c) the amount of straightening of the curve that has to be allowed for when the wood is cooled, if a specified radius of 50 mm has to be achieved.

2 *Testing the Hardness of Abrasive Paper*

Abrasive papers are commonly used in industry, schools and the home. Investigate how well they do their job and how long their working life is. You will need to establish a simple piece of test equipment that measures:

(a) how much material is removed in a given time;

(b) the working life of the abrasive paper.

What types of abrasive papers are there and what are the differences between them? How are abrasive papers graded in coarseness?

3 *The Use of Fillers in Polymers*

Fillers are often added to polymers to improve the mechanical properties and also reduce material costs. Use polyester resin as your test material and compare its properties when mixed with different fillers in varying proportions. Can you establish an optimum percentage of filler that would minimise the quantity of resin used and improve some mechanical properties?

You could try the following fillers: sand, plaster of Paris and sawdust.

You will need to establish one mechanical property that you are going to test, bearing in mind the test facilities that you have at school.

4 *Electroplating*

Mild steel articles rust very easily and are often plated to resist corrosion. Examine the problems associated with plating a small mild steel article. You will need advice from your teacher to establish a process which is feasible within your school, but copper plating and nickel plating do not present much difficulty.

How important is the surface preparation of the steel and how is this best achieved? How does current density (amperes per cm^2 of article) affect the quality of the plating?

Find out what is meant by electroforming and what it can be used for.

34

5 *Evaluating a Domestic Machine*

A domestic vacuum cleaner is a common machine. Examine the external parts and fittings of the machine and identify the materials used. Compile a table of parts and give reasons for the choice of materials, using the following headings.

Name of part	Name of material	Possible reasons for use	Is the material coated? With what and why?

Make a sketch of the machine and label the parts.

Examples of Major Projects

Note Read all relevant safety literature and advise pupils accordingly before they embark on their major projects.

Project Brief 1 (CSE)

PROBLEM

Motor cars frequently have components made of different metals. Where these metals are in contact, corrosion is accelerated. Investigate this aspect of corrosion and identify the metal to metal boundaries most likely to lead to corrosion. Suggest ways in which corrosion can be minimised.

POSSIBLE STARTING POINTS

Choose a particular model of car and use this as a basis for your investigation. Find out the areas where different metals are in contact and identify these metals. Use other samples of the same metals in test situations to discover the likely corrosion problems.

Corrosion is electrical in nature and this should form the basis of the corrosion measurements. Decide the best methods of obtaining the measurements and the equipment that will be necessary.

QUESTIONS TO BE ANSWERED
1 What type of test rig is most suitable?
2 How is the corrosion measured?
3 What differences in measurements were achieved with the metal boundaries?
4 Which metal boundaries would lead to:
   (a) maximum corrosion?
   (b) minimum corrosion?
5 Can you recommend a method of reducing this type of corrosion?

Project Brief 2 (CSE)

PROBLEM

Despite the fact that most of the paper industry is fully mechanised, there is still a demand for high quality hand-made paper. The aim of this project is to identify the problems associated with the making of paper by hand.

POSSIBLE STARTING POINTS

Paper is basically cellulose fibres bound together with certain ceramic materials. A hand-making method needs to separate the fibres in order to make a pulp.

You will need to design a simple piece of apparatus that will convert the pulp into sheet form. From your observations you could later develop this into a more sophisticated process.

QUESTIONS TO BE ANSWERED

1 What different sources of cellulose fibre are available?
2 How can the paper be pressed and dried?
3 What additives are required to give different properties to various qualities of paper?
4 How is the 'watermark' fixed in the paper?
5 What is meant by the 'dry-fibre' process and what important consequences follow from such advances?

Project Brief 3 (CSE)

PROBLEM

It is necessary to mass produce transistor cases as economically as possible. The dimensions of the case are given below. The aim of this project is to investigate the most suitable method of making these cases. For this project you may choose the metal you consider to be the easiest to form.

POSSIBLE STARTING POINTS

Investigate all the possible methods of forming your choice of metal. Try cold-forming techniques first as this may avoid problems of working with hot metal. Remember that cold forming requires a ductile material and considerable force.

QUESTIONS TO BE ANSWERED

1 What method of forming is most suitable?
2 How can the pressure be applied?
3 How can the moulds be manufactured?
4 If heat is necessary how can this best be applied?
5 Is quality control necessary?
6 How much material is wasted?

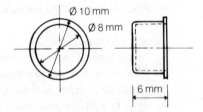

Fig. 10 Transistor case dimensions

Project Brief 4 (CSE/O level)

PROBLEM

The effect of heat on a thermoplastic is to soften it. In this state the material is capable of being formed easily into a desired shape. This softening temperature also determines the service conditions of the product. Design a piece of apparatus to determine the load/extension curve of polymers at different temperatures.

You will need a suitable heater and you must begin by establishing the maximum temperatures involved. The heater must be mounted so that it does not interfere with the method of applying the load.

QUESTIONS TO BE ANSWERED

1 How can you ensure that the sample is evenly heated?
2 How can you measure the temperature?
3 How can you measure the extension?
4 Make a chart showing the temperature and extensions obtained, and from it state the temperature range most suitable for the service conditions of each sample tested.

Project Brief 5 (O level)

PROBLEM

In most modern central-heating systems, copper is nearly always used for pipework even though it is an expensive metal and is often in short supply. The purpose of this project is to investigate the possibilities of replacing copper tube with a modern polymer material.

POSSIBLE STARTING POINTS

Locate a range of plastics which can be easily bought in tubular form. Any replacement material will need to be resistant to heat and capable of being joined to standard metal fittings.

Investigate existing methods of joining pipes to fittings. How many of these methods are suitable for use with polymer materials? Devise alternative methods of joining polymer tubing to other fittings.

QUESTIONS TO BE ANSWERED

1 Rigidity will be important for structural reasons. How do the properties of your materials alter at high temperatures?
2 What implications arise due to the thermal expansion of polymers?
3 Is the material liable to 'creep' and is this important?

Project Brief 6 (O Level)

PROBLEM

Standard soldering irons can easily overheat if they are left on continually. Apart from wasting electricity, the life of the heating element is reduced and the bit oxidises, which means it has to be cleaned and re-tinned.

Design a thermostat for a low-voltage soldering iron to be used for soldering electronic components only.

POSSIBLE STARTING POINTS

Investigate the thermostat operating temperature and the temperature range necessary. Do not forget that the purpose of the iron is to conduct its heat to the wire being soldered. Investigate different types of thermostat but bear in mind that the operating temperature may make some of them unsuitable.

QUESTIONS TO BE ANSWERED
1   Which type of thermostat is most suitable?
2   What is the most suitable position in the circuit for the thermostat?
3   How could the thermostat be incorporated into the iron?
4   What temperature range does the thermostat operate at? (Allow for the heat loss between the bit and the element.)

A Useful Literature

Books on Metals

Many existing science and craft pupil texts cover much of the basic knowledge concerned with metal extraction, refining and production. In addition the following may be found useful.

Corrosion – Attack and Defence, C. Gorham (British Steel Corporation)
A valuable source of background information stressing the chemical nature of corrosion and methods of corrosion resistance. Provides the details for crevice corrosion as used in the module.

Metals and Alloys, Nuffield Chemistry Background Book (Longman)
Useful pupil text probably already available in the chemistry department library.

Metals in the Modern World, Edward Slade (Aldus)
A very thorough look at crystal structure, deformation, extraction, refining and forming. A valuable background book.

Shaping Metals, Bill Gunston (Macdonald Educational)
Written as a pupil text, it is graphically well presented and attractive. It covers simple crystal structure and metal deformation as well as up-to-date methods of forming and shaping.

Structure, Foreground Chemistry No. 7 (Heinemann Educational)
Useful pupil text.

The New Science of Strong Materials, J. E. Gordon (Penguin)
Useful background book, discusses to some depth the atoms and molecules on which mechanical properties depend. A wide range of materials is covered in an easy-to-read, witty text.

The Structure of Substances, Nuffield Chemistry Background Book (Longman)
Useful pupil text probably already available in the chemistry department library.

Which Metals? Pedley and Gorham (British Steel Corporation)
Describes extraction, crystal structure, properties and choice of metals for a specific purpose. Provides useful background information for teachers, although intended for pupils aiming at A-level courses. Very worthwhile resources book.

Books on Polymers

There are few resource books on polymers which cover the range of materials that are used in the module. The following are a selection but are limited in the range of materials that they cover.

Chemicals from Nature, Nuffield Chemistry Background Book (Longman)
Pupil text probably already available in the chemistry department.

Giant Molecules, Morris Kaufman (Aldus)
In the same science and technology series as *Metals in the Modern World*, this book covers in depth the technology of plastics, fibres and rubbers. Includes chemical data and a lot of detail about processes. Background book for teachers.

Man-Made Fibres, Nuffield Chemistry Background Book (Longman)

Plastics, Nuffield Chemistry Background Book (Longman)

Plastics for Schools, Peter J. Clarke (Allman)
Written for technical departments and covering mainly processes. The chemistry of polymers is more than adequately covered.

Practical Work with Modern Materials, John Robinson (E. Arnold)
Gives details of chemistry experiments into polymer science. Includes natural and synthetic materials. Probably already available in the chemistry department. Pupil textbook.

The Science of Rubber (Dunlop Education Section)
Imaginatively produced with attractive overlays to explain polymerisation and cross-linking. Covers the range of natural to synthetic rubbers.

Booklets, etc.

A First Look at Plastics (Plastics Institute)
The development of raw materials and their manufacturing processes. A pupil booklet.

Corrosion, Griffin Technical Studies booklet (Griffin and George)
Intended as a series of experiments for the Griffin and George corrosion kit but provides useful information on a variety of experiments on corrosion.

Facts about Man-made Fibres (British Man-Made Fibres Federation)
Not well illustrated but covers many of the common modern fibres.

Metallurgy, Griffin Technical Studies booklet (Griffin and George)
Intended to be used with the Griffin and George metallurgy kit, it nevertheless provides useful information on mechanical testing and crystal structure.

Nuclear Know How (Central Electricity Generating Board)
Free booklet. A comic-strip approach to the structure of atoms. Intended as information on nuclear reactors and excellently illustrated.

Plastics in Schools – Safety and Hazards (Plastics Institute)
A pullout sheet on health hazards and first aid. A must for teachers using plastics. Advisable to buy two and they can be opened out and displayed prominently.

Safety When Using Plastics in Schools (Plastics Institute)
Not so specific as the one above but nevertheless useful.

Sources of Information on Plastics (Plastics Institute)
A catalogue of sources for books, films and organisations.

The Caveman Series (BP Educational Service)
A series of booklets dealing with topics such as forming in a cartoon style.

Thermoplastics in School Craftwork (ICI Plastics Division)
A lot of free literature on similar topics is available.

The Rusting of Steel, Unilever Laboratory Experiment No. 9 (Unilever Education Service)
Two-page leaflet describing ferroxyl indicator solution experiment to show the corrosion of steel.

What are Plastics? Schools Publication No. 9 (ICI Plastics Division)
Covers a lot of the information on plastics required at CSE level. Good pupil text.

B Audio/Visual Aids

Films

Considering Crystals, 16 mins (Unilever – distributed by the National Audio-Visual Aids Library)
Looks at molecular structure, crystal structure and the crystal lattice, and the ways in which they are bonded.

Evidence for Atoms and Molecules (EFVA – distributed by the National Audio-Visual Aids Library)
Useful for the lessons on atomic theory but *Considering Crystals* is perhaps more suitable.

Polymers (ICI)
Introduces the current nomenclature of polymers and illustrates polymerisation and cross-linking. Briefly shows the common methods of forming by following the production of a refrigerator.

Rubber by Design, 27 mins (Shell)
A survey of the way in which scientists and technologists are involved in the chemical design of rubbers to adapt properties for a specific requirement.

Rubber in Engineering (Golden Films)
Describes the properties of rubber which are important in its use as an engineering material.

The Forming of Metals, 28 mins (Shell)
Illustrates a wide range of forming processes such as rolling, forging and extruding. Uses microstructure photographs to illustrate the effects of annealing and work hardening on the grain boundaries of the metals being formed.

The Hardening and Tempering of Steel, 24 mins (BP)
Looks at the metallurgical background of the subject and covers both theoretical and practical aspects with the help of animation.

Working with Thermoplastics (ICI)
A comprehensive look at the forming methods such as injection moulding, blow moulding, extrusion and vacuum forming.

Film catalogues are also available from the following:
British Petroleum;
The British Steel Corporation;
The Institution of Metallurgists;
The Timber Research and Development Association.

Wallcharts

From BP Educational Service: *How We Use Plastics*
Shaping Plastics
The Hardening and Tempering of Carbon Steels
Which Plastics?

From ICI Plastics Division: *How Plastics Help Us*

From the Timber Research and Development Association:
Derivatives of Wood
Moisture Content
Utilisation

From Pictorial Charts Educational Trust:
Chemical Bonding
Earth's Resources
Shapes of Crystals
Structure – Atomic and Ionic

From the Zinc Alloy Die Casters Association:
Zinc Alloy Die Casting

C Useful Addresses

BP Educational Service
Britannic House, Moor Lane, London EC2Y 9BU

British Man Made Fibres Federation
Bridgewater House, 58 Whitworth Street, Manchester M1 6LS

British Steel Corporation
151 Gower Street, London WC1E 6BB

Central Electricity Generating Board
Public Relations Branch, Bankside House, Sumner Street, London SE1

Copper Development Association
Orchard House, Mutton Lane, Potters Bar, Herts

Dunlop Education Section
10 King Street, London SW1Y 6RA

Educational Service of the Plastics and Rubber Institute (ESPRI)
Department of Creative Design, University of Technology, Loughborough, Leicestershire LE11 3TN

Griffin and George Ltd
PO Box 14, Alperton, Wembley, Middlesex

ICI Plastics Division
Bessemer Road, Welwyn Garden City, Herts AL7 1HD

Institution of Metallurgists
Northway House, High Road, Wetstone, London N20 9LW

Lead Development Association
34 Berkeley Square, London W1

National Audio-Visual Aids Library
Paxton Place, Gipsy Road, London SE27 9SR

National Centre for School Technology
Trent Polytechnic, Burton Street, Nottingham NG1 4BU

Pictorial Charts Educational Trust
27 Kirchen Road, London W13 OUD

Plastics Institute
11 Hobart Place, London SW1 0HL

Surplus Buying Agency
Community Buildings, Station Road, Woodhouse, Sheffield S13 7RD

Timber Research and Development Association
Hughden Valley, High Wycombe, Bucks HP14 4ND

Tin Development Association
34 Berkeley Square, London W1

Unilever Education Service
Unilever House, PO Box 68, London EC4P 4BQ

Zinc Alloy Die Casters Association
34 Berkeley Square, London W1